SNOOPY

(features as)

The Literary Ace

Charles M. Schulz

ℛℛ

Printed and bound in Great Britain
for Ravette Publishing Limited,
Unit 3, Tristar Centre,
Star Road, Partridge Green,
West Sussex RH13 8RA
by Cox & Wyman, Berkshire.

ISBN: 1 84161 026 7

PEANUTS

Helen Sweetstory was born on a small farm on April 5, 1950.

I THINK I'LL SKIP ALL THE STUFF ABOUT HER PARENTS AND GRANDPARENTS...THAT'S ALWAYS KIND OF BORING...

2-25

I'LL ALSO SKIP ALL THE STUFF ABOUT HER STUPID CHILDHOOD... I'LL GO RIGHT TO WHERE THE ACTION BEGAN...

It was raining the night of her high-school prom.

SCHULZ

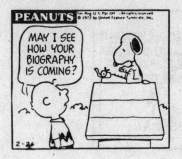

PEANUTS

Helen Sweetstory was born on a small farm on April 5, 1950. It was raining the night of her High-School prom.

"LATER THAT SUMMER SHE WAS THROWN FROM A HORSE..A TALL, DARK STRANGER CARRIED HER BACK TO THE STABLES...WAS THIS THE LOVE SHE HAD BEEN SEEKING? TWO YEARS LATER, IN PARIS, SHE.."

2-29

IN PARIS?! WHAT ABOUT THE TALL, DARK STRANGER? YOU NEVER GO INTO DETAIL!

WHAT KIND OF A BIOGRAPHER ARE YOU?

I'M A GENTLEMAN BIOGRAPHER!

SCHULZ

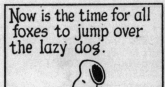
Now is the time for all foxes to jump over the lazy dog.

SOMEHOW, THAT DOESN'T SEEM QUITE RIGHT...

PEANUTS

His wife had always hated his work.

9-18

"You'll never make any money growing toadstools," she complained.

"On the contrary," he declared. "My toadstool business is mushrooming!"

She creamed him with the electric toaster.

SCHULZ

PEANUTS

She wanted to live in Canada.

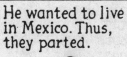

He wanted to live in Mexico. Thus, they parted.

Years later, when asked the reason, she replied simply,

"I just didn't like his latitude!"

PEANUTS

Dutch Waltz, the famous skater, was worried.

His skating partner, Chil Blain, was in love.

While playing a show in Denver, she had become involved with a cowboy named Martin Gale.

THE STORY ISN'T MUCH, BUT THE NAMES ARE GREAT!

4-2

Schulz

PEANUTS

Immediately after he won the golf tournament, he was interviewed on TV.

"This is the most exciting moment of my life!" he said.

"I saw you on TV," said his wife. "I thought the day we got married was the most exciting moment of your life."

In his next tournament, he failed to make the cut.

4-4

PEANUTS

Joe Anthro was an authority on Egyptian and Babylonian culture.

His greatest accomplishment, however, was his famous work on the Throat culture.

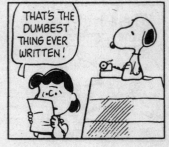

THAT'S THE DUMBEST THING EVER WRITTEN!

ANOTHER FIRST!

PEANUTS

Joe College was getting on in years.

Where had the time gone?

It was hard to believe that he had a son old enough to graduate from High School.

Joe Junior College.

PEANUTS

Gentlemen,
I am submitting a story to your magazine for consideration.

5-4

I have been a subscriber to your magazine for many years.

If you don't publish my story, I am going to cancel my subscription.

So there, too!

SCHULZ

PEANUTS

Kitten Kaboodle was a lazy cat. Actually, all cats are lazy.

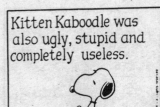

Kitten Kaboodle was also ugly, stupid and completely useless.

But, let's face it, aren't all cats ugly, stupid and completely useless?

I LOVE WRITING ANTI-CAT STORIES!

PEANUTS

And so, once again, Kitten Kaboodle had to admit she had been outsmarted by a dog.

An ordinary dog at that.

DO YOU THINK THERE'S A MARKET FOR ANTI-CAT STORIES?

"PLAYBEAGLE" HAS BOUGHT THE WHOLE SERIES!

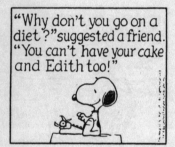

Joe Ceremony
was very short.

4-16

When he entered a
room, everyone had
to be warned not to
stand on Ceremony.

HAHAHAHA!

I'M A GREAT ADMIRER
OF MY OWN WRITING

© 1980 United Feature Syndicate, Inc.

The kidnappers had taken him to a little town called Abeyance.

"Help!" he cried. "I'm being held in Abeyance!"

I GUESS NOT..

Joe Swimming ran a pool service.

1-3

When he and his wife had their first daughter, they couldn't decide on a name.

"How about Chlorine?" suggested Joe.

His wife hit him with a pool sweep.

© 1981 United Feature Syndicate, Inc.

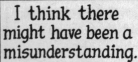

Dear Contributor,

Thank you for considering us with your manuscript.

Has it ever occurred to you that you may be the worst writer in the history of the world?

3-12

I HAVE A UNIQUE COLLECTION OF REJECTION SLIPS...

They could never agree on anything.

4-6

"Why don't we truck on down to the bike shop?" she asked.

"No," he said. "Let's bike on down to the truck shop."

© 1982 United Feature Syndicate, Inc.

Their marriage counselor was not at all encouraging.

SCHULZ

Beauty Tips

© 1982 United Feature Syndicate, Inc.

5-5

HOW CAN YOU WRITE A COLUMN ABOUT BEAUTY?

YOU'RE NOT BEAUTIFUL!

Cute Tips

SCHULZ

Beauty Tips

Always remember that beauty is only skin deep.

© 1982 United Feature Syndicate, Inc.

5-10

fur deep.

Beauty Tips

Always remember
that beauty is
only fur deep.

5-11

© 1982 United Feature Syndicate, Inc.

feather deep.

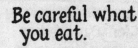

Health Tips.

9-3

When you are looking under your dresser for something you've lost, don't bump your head

And don't say I didn't warn you.

More Health Tips

Eat lots of fruits and vegetables.

Get plenty of rest.

And learn to duck.

"You love hockey more than you love me!" she complained.

11-23

"You love those hockey gloves, and shinguards, and skates and elbow pads more than you love me!"

"That's not true!" he said.

© 1982 United Feature Syndicate, Inc.

"I love you much more than I love my elbow pads."

IT'S VERY EASY TO NEGLECT WRITING LETTERS OF APPRECIATION

THIS IS A GOOD TIME OF YEAR TO WRITE AND TELL SOMEONE HOW MUCH THEY HAVE REALLY MEANT TO YOU...

12-30

Dear Supper Dish,

© 1983 United Feature Syndicate, Inc. 8-9

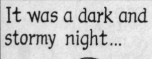

11-22

He was a huge man with a fierce and wild expression, and eyes

like

a teeny tiny little yellow bird.

11-30

"I used to think you were a great engineer," she said.

8-14

"Once, I even loved you..."

"But you've gotten too big for your bridges."

Other PEANUTS™ titles published by Ravette ...

Snoopy Features as ...

The Flying Ace	1 84161 027 5	£2.99
The Matchmaker	1 84161 028 3	£2.99
The Fitness Fanatic	1 84161 029 1	£2.99

Snoopy Laughter and Learning series
wipe clean pages
(a fun series of story and activity books for preschool and infant school children)

available July 2000

Read with Snoopy	1 84161 016 X	£2.50
Write with Snoopy	1 84161 017 8	£2.50
Count with Snoopy	1 84161 018 6	£2.50
Colour with Snoopy	1 84161 019 4	£2.50

PEANUTS™ Anniversary Treasury
(224 pages featuring some of Charlie Brown's favourite strips in colour and black & white)

available August 2000   1 84161 021 6   £9.99

You Really Don't Look 50, Charlie Brown
(over 500 daily and Sunday strips and a series of Charles Schulz essays celebrating this anniversary year).

available Sept 2000   1 84161 020 8   £6.99

All PEANUTS™ books are available from your local bookshop or from the address below. Just tick the titles required and send the form with your payment to:-

BBCS, P.O. Box 941, Kingston upon Hull HU1 3YQ
24-hr telephone credit card line 01482 224626

Prices and availability are subject to change without prior notice.

Please enclose a cheque or postal order made payable to BBCS to the value of the cover price of the book and allow the following for postage and packing:-

UK & BFPO:	£1.95 (weight up to 1kg)		3-day delivery
	£2.95 (weight over 1kg up to 20kg)		3-day delivery
	£4.95 (weight up to 20kg)		next day delivery
EU & Eire:	Surface Mail:	£2.50 for first book & £1.50 for subsequent books	
	Airmail:	£4.00 for first book & £2.50 for subsequent books	
USA:	Surface Mail:	£4.50 for first book & £2.50 for subsequent books	
	Airmail:	£7.50 for first book & £3.50 for subsequent books	
Rest of the World:	Surface Mail:	£6.00 for first book & £3.50 for subsequent books	
	Airmail:	£10.00 for first book & £4.50 for subsequent books	

Name: ....

Address: ....

....

....

Cards accepted: Visa, Mastercard, Switch, Delta, American Express

Expiry date .... Signature ....